1.95

An Educational Coloring Book
of
SOUTHWEST INDIANS

MW00903594

EDITOR
Linda Spizzirri

ILLUSTRATIONS
Peter M. Spizzirri
E. Lisle Reedstrom

COVER ART
Peter M. Spizzirri

CONTENTS

An Educational Coloring Book of SOUTHWEST INDIANS • Published by SPIZZIRRI PUBLISHING, INC.,
P.O. BOX 9397, RAPID CITY, SOUTH DAKOTA 57709. No part of this publication may be reproduced by
any means without the express written consent of the publisher. All national and international rights reserved
on the entire contents of this publication.
Printed in U.S.A.

TRIBE NAME:	JICARILLA APACHE
LANGUAGE:	ATHAPASCAN
WHERE THEY LIVED:	SOUTHEASTERN COLORADO AND NORTHERN NEW MEXICO
KIND OF HOUSE:	POLE FRAME WICKIUPS COVERED WITH BARK, THATCH, AND SOMETIMES SKINS
WHAT THEY ATE:	BUFFALO, DEER, OTHER GAME. CORN, BEANS, MELONS, PEAS, PINE NUTS, BERRIES, SEEDS, FRUITS, AND ROOTS.
INTERESTING FACTS:	It is thought, that the Jacarilla originally migrated from the Canadian eastern Rocky Mountains. They settled in the Plains and hunted buffalo. They were driven west, to southern Colorado and northern New Mexico, when the Comanche and Caddoan Indian tribes acquired firearms. Because they were close to the Pueblo Indians, they learned how to grow crops. The Plains and Pueblo influence is distinctive in the Jicarilla Apache. Jicarilla means "little basket". The name was probably acquired because of the fine basketry they made, which included water-tight vessels.

A WARRIOR AND HIS HORSE

TRIBE NAME:	TAOS
LANGUAGE:	TIWA OF THE TANOAN LANGUAGE
WHERE THEY LIVED:	NORTHEAST OF SANTA FE, NEW MEXICO
KIND OF HOUSE:	FIVE TO SIX STORY ADOBE HOUSES WITH ROOFS MADE OF POLES COVERED WITH DIRT AND GRASS
WHAT THEY ATE:	CORN, BEANS, SQUASH, WILD FRUITS AND VEGETABLES, RABBITS, DEER, BUFFALO, TURKEYS
INTERESTING FACTS:	The Taos are thought to be descendants of the Chaco-Canyon cliff dwellers who moved to the Taos Valley in the thirteenth century.

The grand five and six story houses were built by the men and plastering was finished by the women. Each story was built smaller than the story below it. The lower levels were accessed only by ladders that could be pulled up through the roof. This kept the Taos safely above their enemies. Two large house groupings faced each other across Taos Creek. As the northern most Pueblo, Taos became the center of trade between the Pueblo tribes and the Plains Indians.

ELDERS WEARING RAINBOW BLANKETS

TRIBE NAME:	JEMEZ
LANGUAGE:	TOWA OF THE TANOAN LANUGUAGE
WHERE THEY LIVED:	NORTHWEST OF ALBUQUERQUE, NEW MEXICO ON THE JEMEZ RIVER
KIND OF HOUSE:	ONE OR TWO STORY ADOBE BRICK HOUSES WITH ROOFS OF PINE LOGS. PLASTERED WALLS AND ADOBE BRICK FLOORS
WHAT THEY ATE:	DEER, ELK, ANTELOPE, CACTUS FRUITS, VARIOUS GREENS; GREW CROPS OF CORN, SQUASH, BEANS AND MELON
INTERESTING FACTS:	The religious leader, call cacique, was the tribal leader. It was his responsibility to coordinate celebrations and take care of the tribe. He was assisted in his lifetime job by several governors. New governors were appointed each year. The Jemez women wore distinctive black dresses that wrapped over the right shoulder, under the left arm and was belted with brightly dyed yarns.

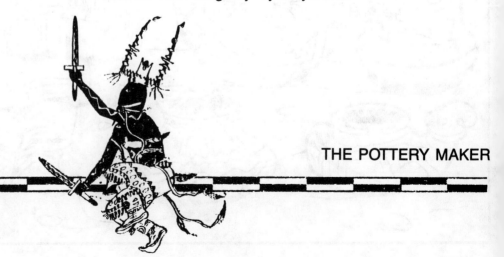

THE POTTERY MAKER

6

TRIBE NAME:	MESCALERO APACHE
LANGUAGE:	ATHAPASCAN
WHERE THEY LIVED:	SOUTHERN NEW MEXICO, WESTERN TEXAS, NORTHERN MEXICO
KIND OF HOUSE:	BUFFALO HIDE TIPIS, OR WICKIUPS OF POLES AND THATCH OR BRUSH
WHAT THEY ATE:	BUFFALO, MESCAL, CORN, BEANS, SQUASH, PRICKLY PEAR, LOCUST BLOSSOMS, SEEDS, NUTS, GRAPES, AND BERRIES.
INTERESTING FACTS:	As far back as 1200 A.D. the Mescalero came from the north. They exchanged buffalo meat and skins for Pueblo farm products. They lived in buffalo hide tipis, like the Plains Indians. They became farmers and gatherers, but after they got horses in the 1600's, the buffalo hunt and raiding parties made them masters of the Southern Plains. The tribe was named after a notorious food they made called "mescal". The mescal was made by baking the base of the agave plant in a pit for several days. The sweet mescal was able to be stored for eating later.

HUNTING THE BUFFALO

TRIBE NAME:	ISLETA
LANGUAGE:	TIWA OF THE TANOAN LANGUAGE
WHERE THEY LIVED:	SOUTH OF ALBUQUERQUE, NEW MEXICO
KIND OF HOUSE:	ADOBE BRICK
WHAT THEY ATE:	CORN, BEANS, WHEAT, FRUITS, NUTS, AND GAME INCLUDING OCCASIONAL BUFFALO
INTERESTING FACTS:	Isleta is a Spanish word which means "little island" and refers to the Pueblo's original location on a small island between the Rio Grande River and one of its tributaries (branches). The location eventually filled in with silt. Their present location has been home since the explorer, Coronado visited their Pueblo in 1540.

All of the Pueblo tribes are rich with customs and centuries of tradition. The many Isleta ceremonies were held in a special building, called the "kiva", or in the central plaza.

The Isleta were farmers and craftsmen who planted their crops, made pottery, and wove cotton belts, blankets, kilts, and leggings. Occasionally they ventured into the plains to hunt buffalo.

THE SPANISH ARRIVE

TRIBE NAME:	ACOMA
LANGUAGE:	KERESAN
KIND OF HOUSE:	A CONTINUOUS 1000 FT., 2-3 STORY, ADOBE
WHAT THEY ATE:	CORN, TURKEYS, RABBITS, DEER, WILD NUTS, BERRIES AND FRUIT SUCH AS PRICKLY PEAR CACTUS FRUIT
INTERESTING FACTS:	The Acoma village was established approximately 1200 A.D. This very old village is one of the oldest continuously inhabited (lived in) villages in the United States. The 1000-foot long terraced Pueblo was divided into individual family living quarters, much like a modern apartment building is today. The bottom level was used for storage and ladders were used to reach the upper living quarters. The Acoma were mainly farmers. The men did some weaving and working with silver. The women, however, were distinctive pottery makers with the reputation of being North America's best.

WOMEN GRINDING CORN

TRIBE NAME:	ZUNI
LANGUAGE:	ZUNI
WHERE THEY LIVED:	SOUTHWEST OF GALLUP, NEW MEXICO
KIND OF HOUSE:	BUILDINGS UP TO FIVE STORIES OF ADOBE AND STONE; PLASTERED WITH ADOBE INSIDE AND OUT AND THEN WHITE WASHED
WHAT THEY ATE:	CORN, BEANS, SQUASH, CORN MUSH AND BREAD, DEER, ANTELOPE AND RABBITS
INTERESTING FACTS:	The Zuni developed complex social and religious societies. The Pueblo was ruled by a council made up of leaders of the various societies. As with other Pueblo tribes, the katcina (kachina) was one of the most important societies. All adult males of the Zuni tribe were members of this society.

The most important celebration of the year was the winter solstice where priests, wearing huge 12-foot high masks, blessed the Pueblo for the coming year. The tribes staple food was corn. The Zuni men are known to have grown at least six different varieties of corn.

Today the Zuni have the distinction of being the largest Pueblo tribe.

TENDING THE FIELDS

TRIBE NAME:	NAVAJO
LANGUAGE:	ATHAPASCAN
WHERE THEY LIVED:	ARIZONA, NEW MEXICO, AND UTAH
KIND OF HOUSE:	CALLED HOGANS, BUILT MUCH LIKE A LOG CABIN WITH WALLS BUILT UP AROUND FOUR VERTICAL POLES. WALLS OFTEN COVERED WITH EARTH. DOMED ROOF HAD SMOKE HOLE OPENING.
WHAT THEY ATE:	CORN, BEANS, SQUASH, PINE NUTS, CACTUS FRUIT, WILD POTATOES, GREENS, SEEDS, GAME MEAT AND LIVESTOCK
INTERESTING FACTS:	There were more than 60 Navajo clans. As was common, each person belonged to the clan of his mother and was forbidden to marry anyone from his mother's or father's clan. When a young couple married, they lived near her mother but a man never was in a room with, or talked to, his mother-in-law.

The Navajo came to the southwest as hunters and quickly learned farming from the Pueblo tribes. They also borrowed from the Pueblo religious customs. The Navajo raised livestock, hunted, trapped, and farmed. The women made fine pottery and basketry. They learned weaving from the Pueblos, but soon were recognized for their own imaginative designs and dyes.

SHAMAN CREATING
A DRY PAINTING

TRIBE NAME:	HOPI
LANGUAGE:	SHOSHONEAN
WHERE THEY LIVED:	NORTHEASTERN ARIZONA
KIND OF HOUSE:	ADOBE PLASTERED OVER ONE OR TWO STORY HOUSES OF SAND STONE
WHAT THEY ATE:	GREW CORN, SQUASH, BEANS, AND COTTON; GATHERED NUTS AND BERRIES; HUNTED SMALL GAME
INTERESTING FACTS:	The Hopi Pueblo was established in 1150. The farthest west of all Pueblo tribes, the peaceful Hopi Indians developed a very complex social and ceremonial life. Each child had a ceremonial parent, of their same sex, who saw them through the various ceremonies as they reached adulthood. The most important rite for girls was the puberty rite which included wrapping their hair into the beautiful "squash blossom" or "Butterfly" whorl. The maidens wore their hair like this until they married.

The Hopi considered the winter solstice as their most important ceremony. More popularly known, was their harvest time (Niman) festival, where the snake and antelope societies used live snakes for their weather control ceremony.

HOPI SNAKE DANCE

TRIBE NAME:	CHIRICAHUA APACHE
LANGUAGE:	ATHAPASCAN
WHERE THEY LIVED:	ARIZONA, NEW MEXICO, AND MEXICO
KIND OF HOUSE:	DOME-SHAPED WICKIUPS MADE OF POLES COVERED WITH GRASS. HIDES WERE ADDED IN BAD WEATHER
WHAT THEY ATE:	MOUNTAIN GOATS, GAME, AGAVE, BEANS, CACTUS FRUIT, YUCCA, NUTS, SEEDS, BERRIES, AND MESCAL
INTERESTING FACTS:	The Chiricahua had many festivals and ceremonies. The young coming of age was a special social gathering. A girl took part in a four day ceremony, dressed in a special soft deer-skin dress. A young boy had to participate in at least four raids to become an adult warrior. The Chiricahua occupied their territory from 1200 A.D. When the Spanish came in the 1500's conflicts arose. Present day T.V., movies, and novels made the Chiricahua leaders of the 1800's familiar names. Indians who opposed the white mans move west, such as Cochise and Geronimo, became household words.

THE MOUNTAIN SPIRIT DANCER

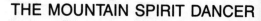

TRIBE:	PIMA
LANGUAGE:	PIMAN DIVISION OF THE UTO-AZ-TECAN LANGUAGE
WHERE THEY LIVED:	SOUTHERN ARIZONA
KIND OF HOUSE:	DOME-SHAPED HOUSES OF POLE FRAMEWORK THEN COVERED WITH THATCH AND EARTH
WHAT THEY ATE:	CORN, BEANS, SQUASH, FRUIT, YUCCA, NUTS, SEEDS, FISH AND GAME
INTERESTING FACTS:	This quiet tribe and their southern neighbors, the Papago, are essentially one people. Their cultures are the same, except for the fact that the Pima had enough water to grow crops. The Papago (desert people) had to rely on hunting and gathering for their food.

The Pima are one of the rare Southwest Indian tribes where each person belonged to the clan of their father. When a young couple married they lived with the groom's family. The Pima liked to adorn themselves with white, red and yellow body paint, turquoise ear ornaments, and tattooing. The women wove baskets and made pottery. The men wove blankets and cotton belts.

WEAVING A GRANARY BASKET

TRIBE NAME:	PAPAGO
LANGUAGE:	PIMAN OF THE UTO-AZTECAN LANGUAGE
WHERE THEY LIVED:	SOUTH OF THE GILA RIVER IN ARIZONA
KIND OF HOUSE:	CIRCULAR HOUSES OF POLE AND THATCH, PARTIALLY UNDERGROUND COVERED WITH EARTH
WHAT THEY ATE:	CORN, BEANS, SQUASH, WILD FRUITS AND VEGETABLES, AND GAME
INTERESTING FACTS:	The Papago were different from the Pima mainly due to the fact that they had no constant water supply. Villages were small, usually consisting of one extended family. When it was time for the rains, they lived by small streams and planted crops. In the fall, they returned to the foothills to camp near wells, and survived by hunting and gathering. Gathering food was a hard task which occupied all of the young. The older tribe members did the craft work of making baskets and weaving. During the fall and winter, trading trips were made to obtain the farm products that they were short on. They exchanged dried meats, dye pigments, and salt.

HARVESTING CRIMSON FRUIT
FROM THE SAGUARO

TRIBE NAME:	MOHAVE
LANGUAGE:	YUMAN OF THE HOKAN LANGUAGE
WHERE THEY LIVED:	BOTH SIDES OF THE LOWER COLORADO RIVER
KIND OF HOUSE:	FLAT-ROOFED HOUSES COVERED WITH ARROW WEED THATCH AND SAND
WHAT THEY ATE:	FISH, CORN, BEANS, SQUASH, PUMPKINS, PINE NUTS, AND GAME
INTERESTING FACTS:	Although the Mohave did not band together in large settlements, they still had a strong sense of tribal brotherhood. They settled on any land in their region suitable for planting and gathering. Fish was an important part of their diet. The Mohave had a reputation for being fierce warriors. They engaged in constant warfare with the Maricopa and Pima. Trading was a very important part of Mohave life. They would even travel hundreds of miles to the coast to obtain seashells. They acted as merchants dealing in pottery, Hopi blankets, dried foods and seashells. The Mohave decorated themselves with artistic face and body painting. The men often wore feathers in their hair.

THE HUNTERS

TRIBE NAME:	YUMA
LANGUAGE:	YUMAN DIVISION OF HOKAN LANGUAGE
WHERE THEY LIVED:	NEAR THE JUNCTION OF COLORADO AND GILA RIVERS
KIND OF HOUSE:	SUMMER: RECTANGULAR POLE HOUSES COVERED WITH ARROW WEED. WINTER: UNDERGROUND LIVING QUARTERS, COVERED WITH A LAYER OF SAND
WHAT THEY ATE:	CORN, SQUASH, BEANS, NUTS, SEEDS, FISH, AND SOME GAME
INTERESTING FACTS:	The Yuma leader was chosen to his position because of his personality and ability to lead. The position was not hereditary (handed down from the father), as in many tribes.

The Yuma planted crops in the flood plains, after the spring waters returned to their normal river banks. Game was scarce, but because they lived so close to the river, fishing was of primary importance. They were also excellent swimmers.

The Yuma were fierce warriors, usually fighting the Pima or Maricopa. The warriors used clubs, bows, stone knives, and hide shields. They also fire-hardened long sticks to use as spears. They did have horses, but considered it unsportsman like to use them in battle.

MEDICINE MAN PAINTING A WARRIOR

TRIBE NAME: COCOPA

LANGUAGE: YUMAN OF THE HOKAN LANGUAGE

WHERE THEY LIVED: ALONG THE COLORADO AND HARDY RIVERS. BY 1500'S FORCED TO MOUTH OF THE COLORADO

KIND OF HOUSE: SUMMER: BRUSH SHELTER
                       WINTER: EARTHEN HOUSES OF POLE FRAMEWORK COVERED WITH THATCH AND EARTH

WHAT THEY ATE: CORN, MESQUITE, BLUE PALM FRUIT, BEANS, AGAVE, MELONS, SEEDS, GAME, FISH, FOWL, AND WILD RICE

INTERESTING FACTS: One of the Cocopa's most important religious ceremonies was their puberty ceremony. The girls got their chins tattooed and the boys got their noses pierced.

When the spring floods were over, crops were planted in the rich flood plains. The tribe not only planted, but gathered, hunted, and did a lot of fishing. Once a year a raft trip was made to collect wild rice from an island on the Hardy River. Large pottery jars were lashed together on small rafts, to transport valuables. Large rafts, used for the major transporting, had a clay floor section where cooking could be done on the raft.

BOY RECEIVING A
PROTECTING AMULET

Educational Coloring Books and
STORY CASSETTES

The only non-fiction coloring book/cassette packages available! The cassettes are not read-alongs. Rather, the educational factual information in the coloring book is utilized and enhanced to create exciting stories. Sound, music, and professional narration stimulate interest and promote reading. Children can color and listen, color alone, or simply listen to the cassette. We are proud to offer these quality products at a reasonable price.

DISPLAY RACKS AVAILABLE. INDIVIDUALLY PACKAGED.

YOUR CHOICE OF 48 TITLES

"ISBN (INTERNATIONAL STANDARD BOOK NUMBER) PREFIX ON ALL BOOKS AND CASSETTES: 0-86545-

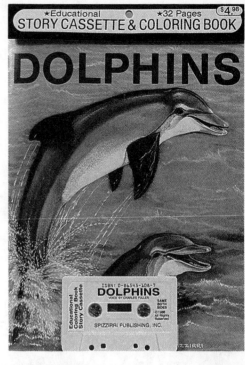

No. 082-X	DINOSAURS	No. 161-3	DOGS	
No. 083-8	Prehistoric SEA LIFE	No. 162-1	HORSES	
No. 084-6	Prehistoric BIRDS	No. 159-1	BIRDS	
No. 085-4	CAVE MAN	No. 147-8	PENGUINS	
No. 086-2	Prehistoric FISH	No. 098-6	STATE BIRDS	
No. 087-0	Prehistoric MAMMALS	No. 163-X	STATE FLOWERS	
No. 097-8	Count/Color DINOSAURS	No. 100-1	MAMMALS	
No. 089-7	PLAINS INDIANS	No. 101-X	REPTILES	
No. 090-0	NORTHEAST INDIANS	No. 158-3	POISONOUS SNAKES	
No. 091-9	NORTHWEST INDIANS	No. 102-8	CATS OF THE WILD	
NO. 092-7	SOUTHEAST INDIANS	No. 103-6	ENDANGERED SPECIES	
No. 093-5	SOUTHWEST INDIANS	No. 157-5	PRIMATES	
No. 094-3	CALIFORNIA INDIANS	No. 104-4	ANIMAL GIANTS	
No. 153-2	ESKIMOS	No. 148-6	ATLANTIC FISH	
No. 152-4	COWBOYS	No. 149-4	PACIFIC FISH	
No. 150-8	COLONIES	No. 105-2	SHARKS	
No. 151-6	PIONEERS	No. 106-0	WHALES	No. 111-7 SPACE EXPLORERS
No. 154-0	FARM ANIMALS	No. 107-9	DEEP-SEA FISH	No. 112-5 PLANETS
No. 095-1	DOLLS	No. 108-7	DOLPHINS	No. 113-3 COMETS
No. 096-X	ANIMAL ALPHABET	No. 109-5	AIRCRAFT	No. 114-1 ROCKETS
No. 160-5	CATS	No. 110-9	SPACE CRAFT	No. 155-9 TRANSPORTATION
				No. 156-7 SHIPS

ALL BOOK CASSETTE PACKAGES $4.98 EACH

LISTEN AND COLOR
LIBRARY ALBUMS

6 Educational Coloring Books
Book/Story Cassettes
In a plastic storage case

We have gathered cassettes and books of related subject matter into individual library albums. Each album will provide a new, in-depth, and lasting learning experience. They are presented in a beautiful binder that will store and protect your collection for years.
We also invite you to pick 6 titles of your chosing and create your own CUSTOM ALBUM.

LIBRARY ALBUMS $34.95 EACH

CHOOSE ANY LIBRARY ALBUM LISTED, OR SELECT TITLES FOR YOUR CUSTOM ALBUM

No. 088-9 Prehistoric Life	No. 116-8 American Indian	No. 164-8 Oceans & Seas	No. 117-6 Air & Space	No. 165-6 Americana
Dinosaurs	Plains Indians	Atlantic Fish	Aircraft	Colonies
Prehistoric Sea Life	Northeast Indians	Pacific Fish	Space Craft	Cowboys
Prehistoric Fish	Northwest Indians	Sharks	Space Explorers	Pioneers
Prehistoric Birds	Southeast Indians	Whales	Planets	State Flowers
Prehistoric Mammals	Southwest Indians	Deep-Sea Fish	Comets	State Birds
Cave Man	California Indians	Dolphins	Rockets	Endangered Species

No. 166-4 Animal Libr #1	No. 167-2 Animal Libr. #2	No. 168-0 Young Students	No. 170-2 New Titles Library	No. 169-9 Custom Library
Poisonous Snakes	Prehistoric Mammals	Animal Alphabet	Eskimos	WE INVITE YOU TO PICK 6 TITLES OF YOUR CHOSING AND CREATE YOUR OWN CUSTOM LIBRARY.
Reptiles	Birds	Counting & Coloring Dinosaurs	State Flowers	
Animal Giants	Farm Animals	Dolls	Penguins	
Mammals.	Endangered Species	Dogs	Atlantic Fish	
Cats of the Wild	Animal Alphabet	Cats	Pacific Fish	
Primates	State Birds	Horses	Farm Animals	